HOME ORGANIST LIBRARY VOLUME 14

Easy Listening

Arranged by Kenneth Baker.

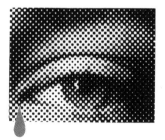

Wise Publications
London/New York/Paris/Sydney

Exclusive Distributors:
Music Sales Limited
8/9 Frith Street, London, W1V 5TZ, England
Music Sales Pty. Limited
120 Rothschild Avenue, Rosebery, NSW 2018, Australia

This book © Copyright 1992 by Wise Publications
Order No. AM88916
ISBN 0-7119-2962-9

Designed by Howard Brown
Cover Photograph by Holly Warburton
Compiled by Peter Evans
Music arranged by Kenneth Baker
Music processed by MSS Studios

Music Sales complete catalogue lists thousands of titles
and is free from your local music book shop, or direct from Music Sales Limited.
Please send a cheque/postal order for £1.50 for postage to
Music Sales Limited, Newmarket Road, Bury St Edmunds, Suffolk IP33 3YB.

Your Guarantee of Quality
As publishers, we strive to produce every book to the highest commercial standards.
The music has been freshly engraved and the book has been carefully designed to minimise
awkward page turns and to make playing from it a real pleasure.
Particular care has been given to specifying acid-free, neutral-sized paper which has not been
elemental chlorine bleached but produced with special regard for the environment.
Throughout, the printing and binding have been planned to ensure a sturdy, attractive publication
which should give years of enjoyment.
If your copy fails to meet our high standards, please inform us and we will gladly replace it.

Printed in the United Kingdom by
JB Offset Printers (Marks Tey) Limited, Marks Tey, Essex.

Contents:

Sometimes When We Touch

Words & Music by Dan Hill & Barry Mann.

Upper: guitar
Lower: flutes
Pedal: 8'
Drums: 8 beat

♩ = 92

stop drums

Tennessee Waltz

Words & Music by Redd Stewart & Pee Wee King.

Upper: clarinet
Lower: flutes
Pedal: 8'
Drums: waltz

♩ = 88

Unchained Melody

Music by Alex North. Words by Hy Zaret.

Upper: oboe
Lower: flutes
Pedal: 8′
Drums: 8 beat

INTERLUDE (ON LOWER)

Lone - ly riv - ers flow to the sea, to the
Lone - ly riv - ers sigh, 'Wait for me, wait for

sea. of the
me!' I'll be com - ing home, wait for

sea.
me.

12

The Hawaiian Wedding Song

Music & Original Hawaiian Lyric by Charles E. King.

English Lyric by Al Hoffman & Dick Manning.

Upper: hawaiian guitar
Lower: flutes
Pedal: 8′
Drums: 8 beat

ne - ver,
I will love you long - er than for -

ev - er.
Now that we are one,

clouds won't hide the sun.
Blue skies of Ha -

wai - i smile on this, our wed - ding day.

stop drums

15

Unforgettable

Words & Music by Irving Gordon.

Upper: trombone
Lower: flutes
Pedal: 8'
Drums: swing

stop drums 17

Portrait Of My Love

Words by David West. Music by Cyril Ornadel.

Upper: piano
Lower: flutes
Pedal: 8′
Drums: 8 beat

♩ = 100

stop drums

Feelings

(Dime)

By Morris Albert & Louis Gaste.

Upper: electric piano
Lower: flutes
Pedal: 8′
Drums: bossa nova

♩ = 100

Stardust

Words by Mitchell Parish. Music by Hoagy Carmichael.

Upper: muted trumpet
Lower: flutes
Pedal: 8'
Drums: swing

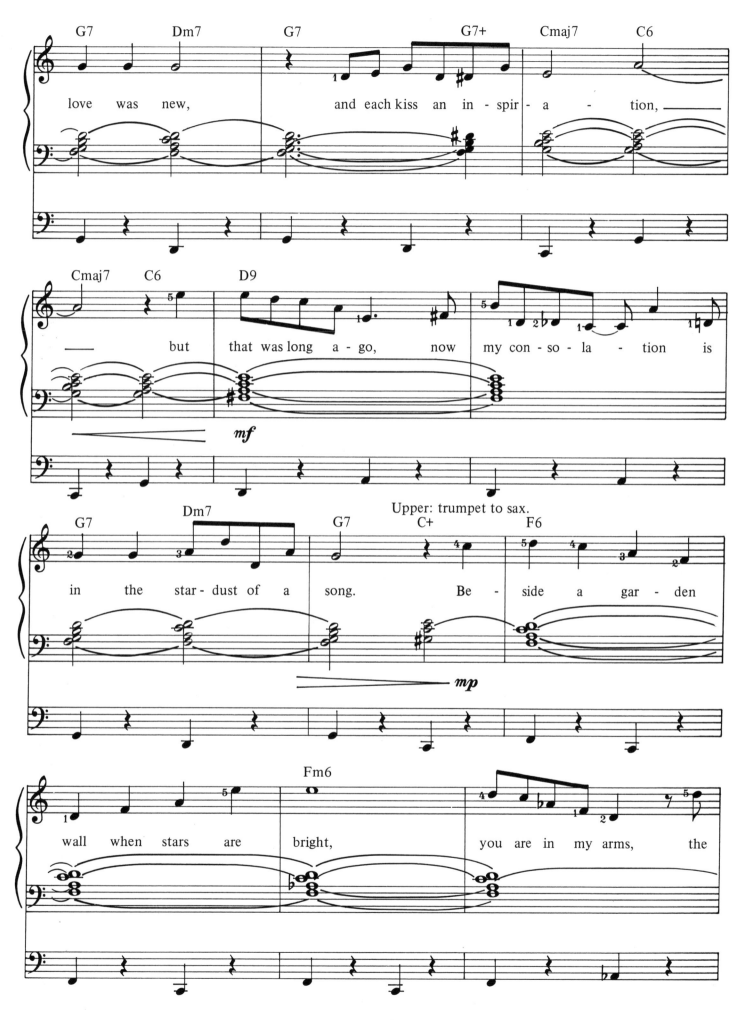

stop drums

It's Impossible

(Somos Novios)

Words by Sid Wayne. Music by A. Manzanero.

Upper: oboe
Lower: flutes
Pedal: 8′
Drums: 8 beat

Raindrops Keep Falling On My Head

Words by Hal David. Music by Burt Bacharach.

Upper: saxophone
Lower: flutes + piano
Pedal: 8'
Drums: swing

31

meet me won't de - feat me, it won't be long ___ till

hap - pi - ness steps up to greet ___ me.

be - cause I'm free.

Noth - in's wor - ry - in' me. ___

Upper: cut musical box

D.C. al Coda

CODA

SLOWER ad lib.

(stop drums)

Killing Me Softly With His Song

Words by Norman Gimbel. Music by Charles Fox.

Upper: oboe
Lower: flutes
Pedal: 8'
Drums: 8 beat

♩ = 108

35

Moulin Rouge Waltz

Words by William Engvick. Music by Georges Auric.

Upper: accordion
Lower: flutes
Pedal: 8′
Drums: waltz

♩ = 88

36

Too Young

Words by Sylvia Dee. Music by Sid Lippman.

Upper: muted trumpet
Lower: flutes
Pedal: 8′
Drums: swing

♩ = 100

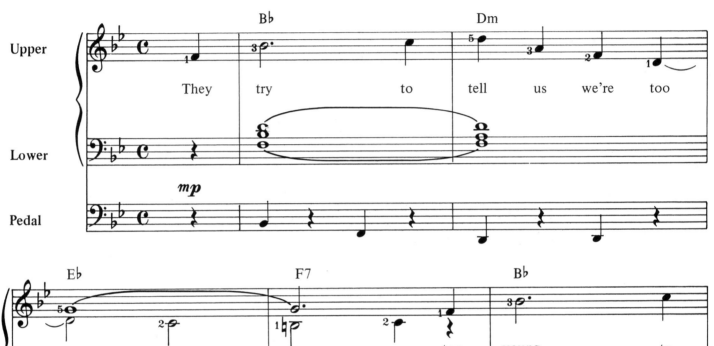

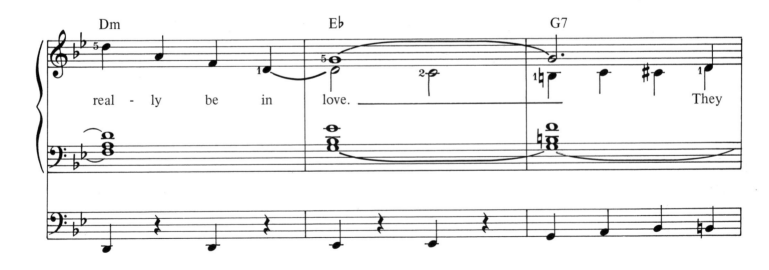

say that love's a word, a word we've on - ly

heard, but can't be - gin to know the mean - ing

cresc.

Upper: trumpet to saxophone

of. And yet we're

f *mp*

not too young to know this

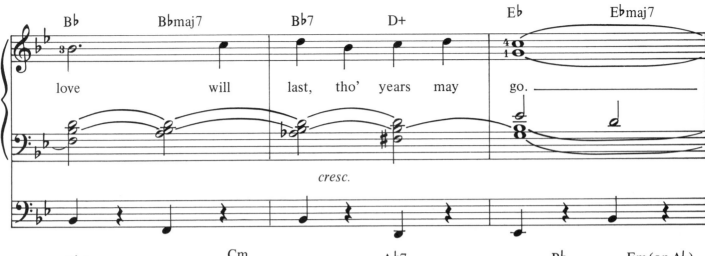

love will last, tho' years may go. ____

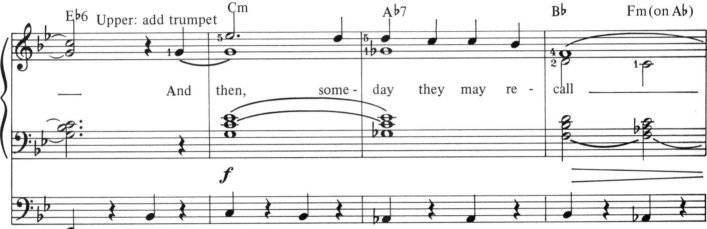

Upper: add trumpet

____ And then, some- day they may re- call ____

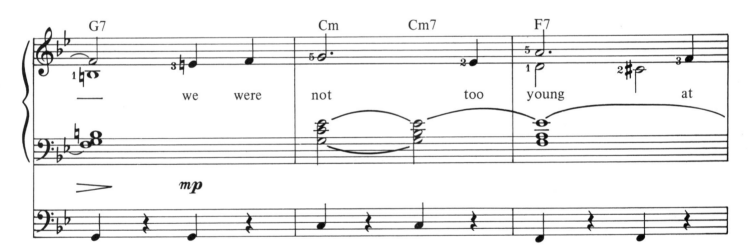

____ we were not too young at

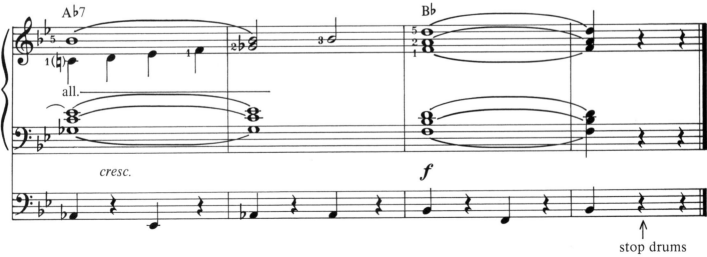

all. ____

stop drums

Amor

Spanish Words by Ricardo Lopez Mendez. English Words by Sunny Skylar.
Music by Gabriel Ruiz.

Upper: flute
Lower: flutes + piano
Pedal: 8′
Drums: beguine

♩ = 112

I'll Know

Words & Music by Frank Loesser.

Upper: violin
Lower: flutes
Pedal: 8′
Drums: 8 beat

♩ = 92

Upper: to string ensemble

stop drums

45

Non Dimenticar

Music by PG Redi. English Lyric by Shelley Dobbins.
Original Italian Lyric by Michele Galdieri.

Upper: accordion
Lower: flutes
Pedal: 8'
Drums: swing

Who Can I Turn To?

Words & Music by Leslie Bricusse & Anthony Newley.

Upper: piano
Lower: flutes
Pedal: 8′
Drums: bossa nova

♩ = 96

Take Me Home, Country Roads

Words & Music by Bill Danoff, Taffy Nivert & John Denver.

Upper: flute
Lower: flutes
Pedal: 8'
Drums: swing

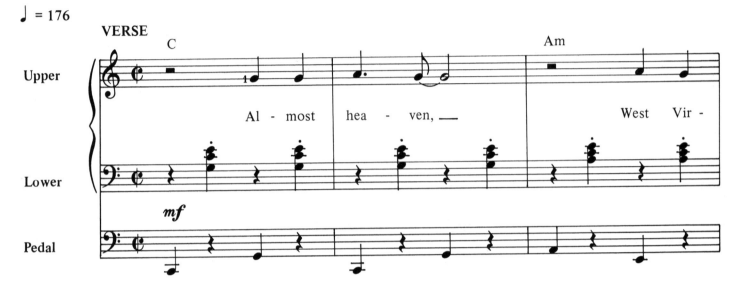

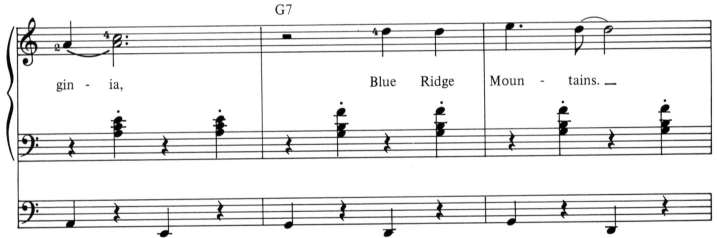

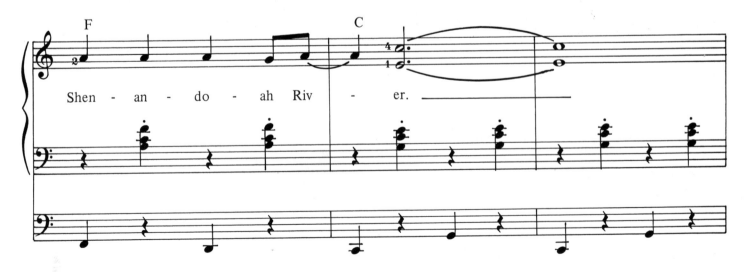

CHORUS

53

place _____ I be - long, _____

_____ West Vir - gin - ia, _____ moun - tain mom-

- ma, _____ take _____ me home _____

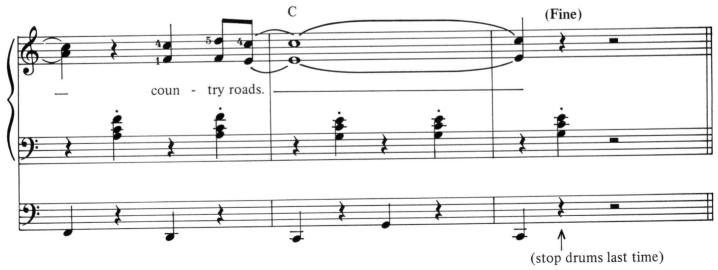

_____ coun - try roads. _____

(Fine)

(stop drums last time)

54

INTERLUDE

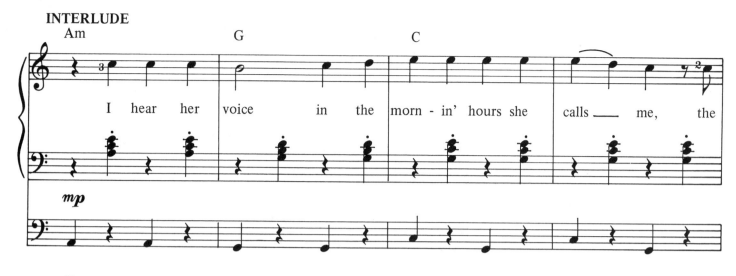

I hear her voice in the morn - in' hours she calls ___ me, the

ra - di - o re - minds me of my home far a - way. And

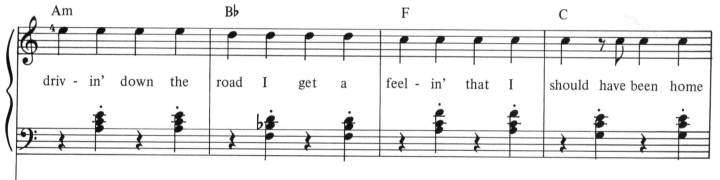

driv - in' down the road I get a feel - in' that I should have been home

D.S. al Fine
Upper: flute to brass

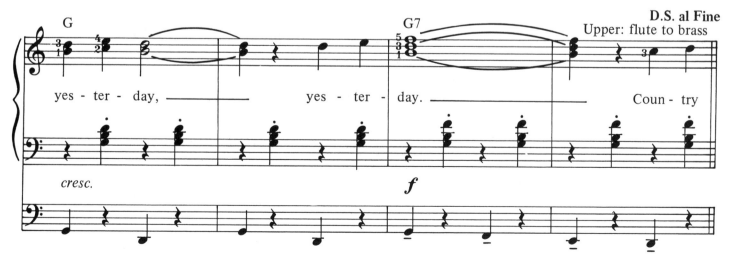

yes - ter - day, ___ yes - ter - day. ___ Coun - try

cresc.   *f*

Can't Smile Without You

Words & Music by Chris Arnold, David Martin & Geoff Morrow.

Upper: organ (with tremolo)
Lower: flutes
Pedal: 8'
Drums: swing

♩ = 104

If You Leave Me Now

Words & Music by Peter Cetera.

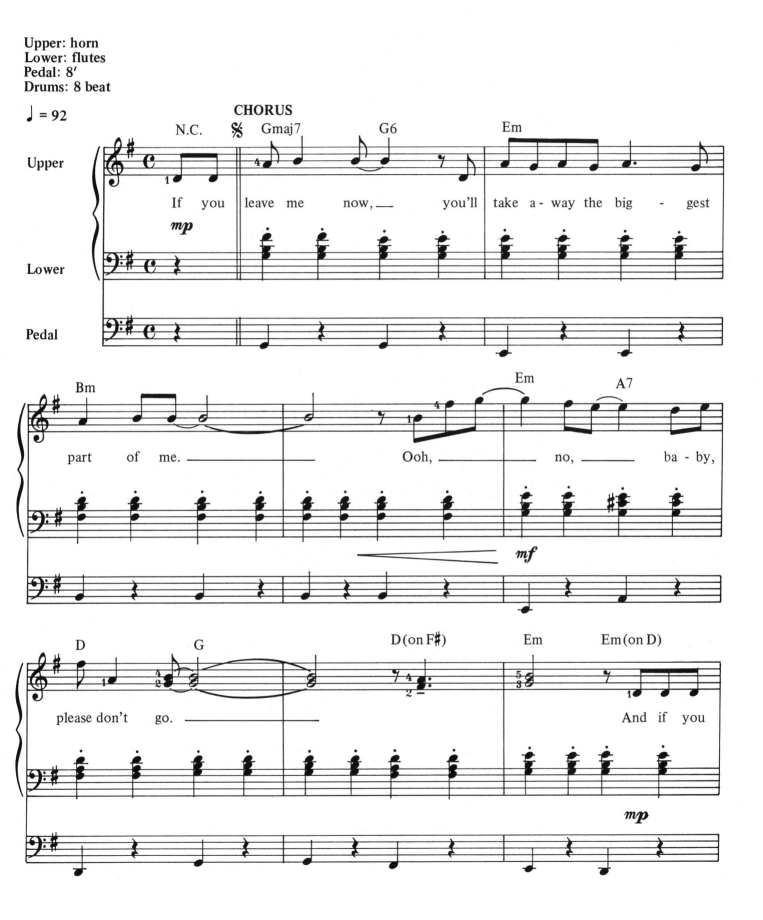

I'm A Dreamer, Aren't We All?

Words & Music by Buddy de Sylva, Lew Brown & Ray Henderson.

Upper: clarinet
Lower: flutes
Pedal: 8'
Drums: swing

♩ = 160

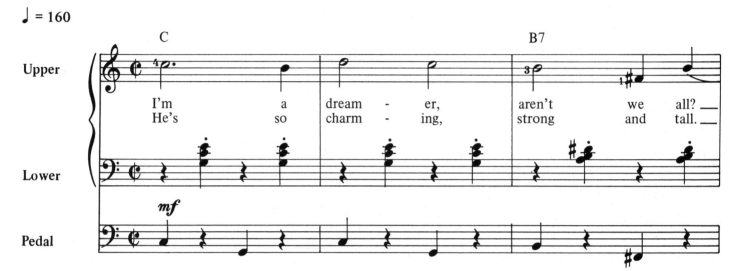

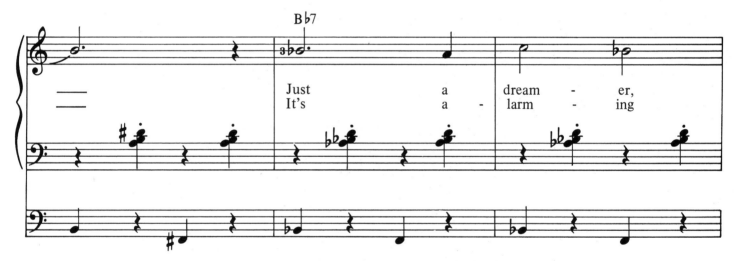

Upper: add piano

Lyrics under the staves:

dreams — each but night it seems my
deal,

sweet - heart comes to call.

then, he is - n't real, and I'm a

fool! But aren't we all?

stop drums

Love's Been Good To Me

Words & Music by Rod McKuen.

Upper: electric piano
Lower: flutes
Pedal: 8'
Drums: bossa nova

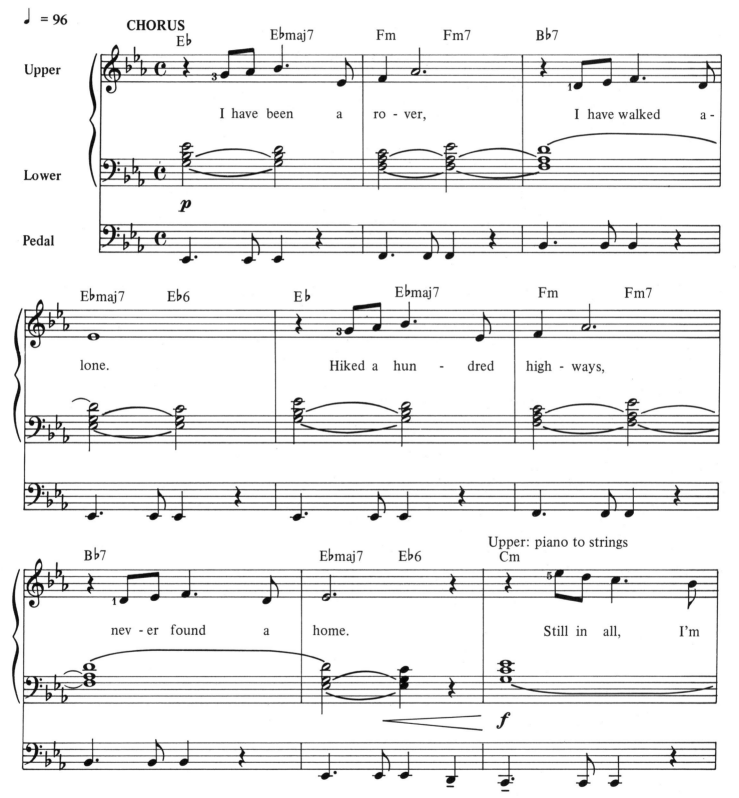

ten - der! Oh, her arms were warm! And she could

smile a - way the thun - der, ___

kiss a - way the rain, and e - ven though she's

D.C. al Fine
Upper: cut strings

gone a - way, you won't hear me com - plain.

King Of The Road

Words & Music by Roger Miller.

Upper: muted trumpet
Lower: piano
Pedal: 8'
Drums: swing

♩ = 112

ev - er - y town,___ and ev - 'ry lock that ain't locked when no - one's a - round,___ I sing,

king of the road,

king of the road,___

king of the road._____

stop drums

Love Is Blue

(L'Amour Est Bleu)

Music by André Popp. Original Words by Pierre Cour.
English Lyric by Bryan Blackburn.

Upper: harpsichord
Lower: flutes
Pedal: 8'
Drums: 8 beat

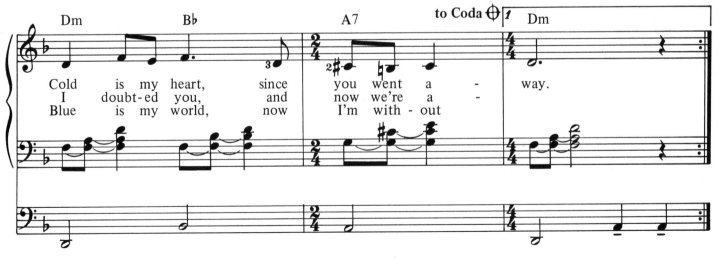

Heartaches

Words by John Klenner. Music by Al Hoffman.

Upper: string ensemble
Lower: flutes + piano
Pedal: 8'
Drums: swing

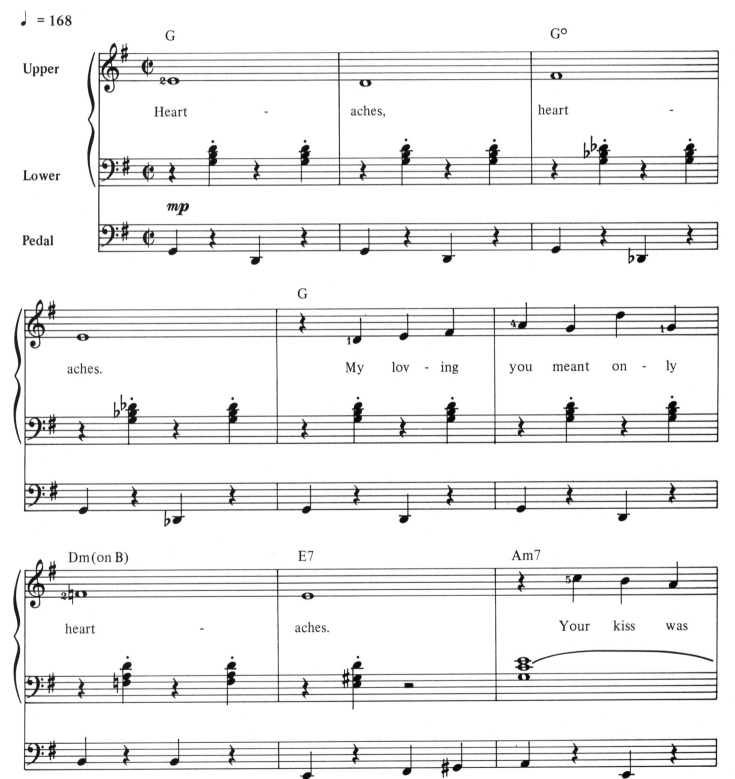

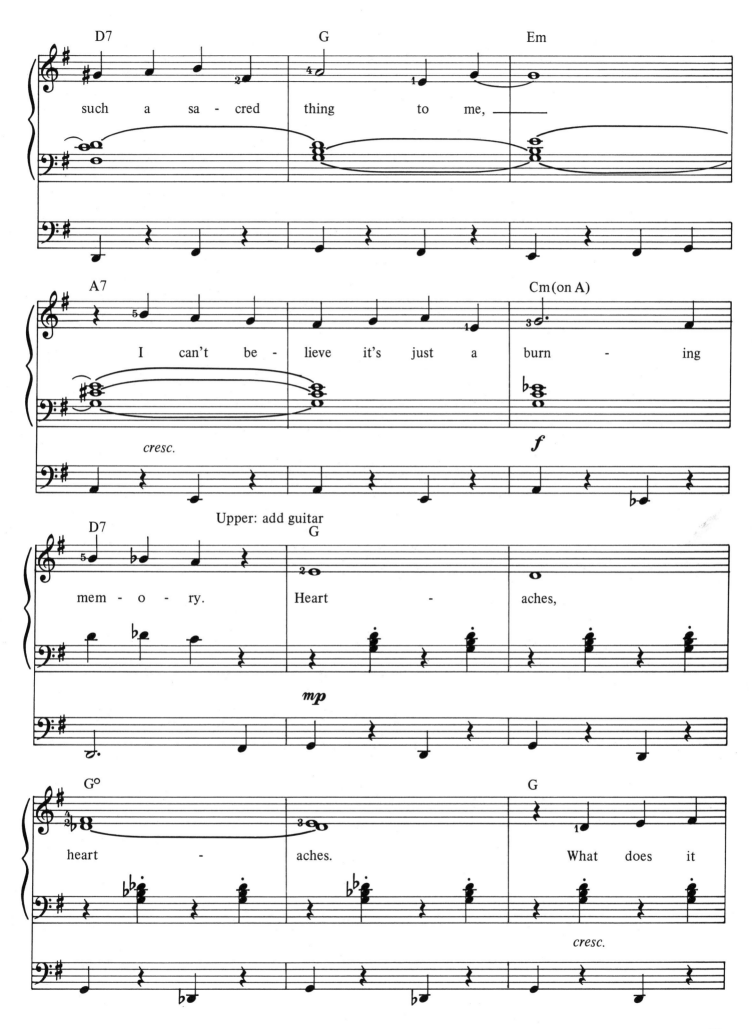

such a sa - cred thing to me,

I can't be - lieve it's just a burn - ing

cresc. *f*

Upper: add guitar

mem - o - ry. Heart - aches,

mp

heart - aches. What does it

cresc.

73

The Look Of Love

Words by Hal David. Music by Burt Bacharach.

Upper: brass ensemble
Lower: flutes + piano
Pedal: 8'
Drums: 8 beat

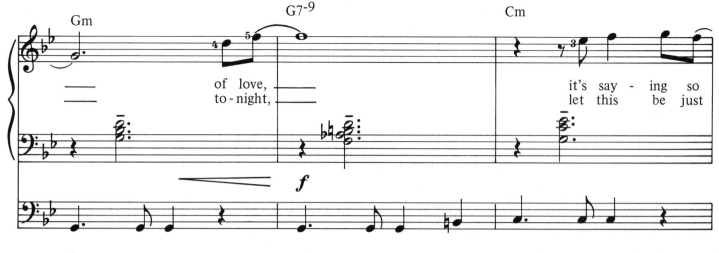

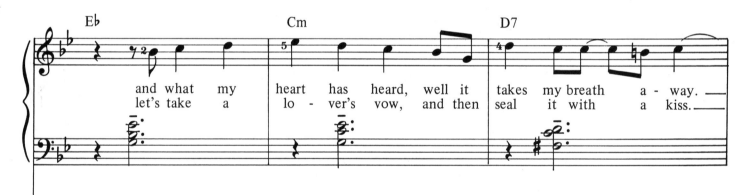

Watch What Happens

Words by Norman Gimbel. Music by Michel Legrand.

Upper: organ
Lower: flutes + piano
Pedal: 8'
Drums: bossa nova